This is . . . .'s book
You may just within it look,
But you'd better not do more,
For the devil's at the door,
And he will snatch at fingering hands;
Look behind you—there he stands.

VOICES

an anthology of poems and pictures

edited by GEOFFREY SUMMERFIELD

the first book

Rand McNally & Company · CHICAGO

Acknowledgements

For permission to reprint copyrighted material in this volume, grateful acknowledgement is made to the following:

Aldine Publishing Company: For "The Chaffinch Map of Scotland" and "The Computer's First Christmas Card," both reprinted from Edwin Morgan, *The Second Life* (Edinburgh: Edinburgh University Press, 1968); copyright © by Edwin Morgan and Edinburgh University Press.

Atheneum House, Inc.: For "Ululation" by Eve Merriam. Copyright © 1964 by Eve Merriam. From *It Doesn't Always Have To Rhyme.* Used by permission of Atheneum Publishers, Inc.

Collins-Knowlton-Wing, Inc.: For "The Two Witches" by Robert Graves from *Good Housekeeping Magazine* (November 1961) and "What Did I Dream?" by Robert Graves from *Poems 1914-1926.* All reprinted by permission of Collins-Knowlton-Wing, Inc. Copyrights © 1923, 1929, and 1961 by Robert Graves.

Corinth Books, Inc.: For "Brian O Linn" from *Irish Street Ballads*, edited by Colm O'Lochlainn. Copyright © 1960 by Corinth Books.

Allen Curnow, Roger Oppenheim and The Caxton Press: For "Chant Before Battle" translated from the Maori by Allen Curnow and Roger Oppenheim.

Dais: For "Blackfoot Prayer to the Four Directions," first published in *The Prayers of Man* edited by Di Nola.

Dodd, Mead & Company, Inc.: For "I Meant To Do My Work Today" by Richard LeGallienne. Reprinted by permission of Dodd, Mead & Company, Inc. from *The Lonely Dancer* by Richard LeGallienne. Copyright 1913 by Dodd, Mead & Company; copyright renewed.

Doubleday & Company, Inc.: For "Loneliness" and "Persistence" by Basho, "The Dragonfly" by Chisoku, "The New Moon," and "Pity" by Issa, "Sounds" by Wafū, and "The Wild Geese Leave" by Yasui, all translated by Harold G. Henderson, from *An Introduction to Haiku* by Harold G. Henderson. Copyright © 1958 by Harold G. Henderson. Reprinted by permission of Doubleday & Company, Inc. For "The Lady and the Bear," © 1951 by Theodore Roethke, "The Meadow Mouse," © 1963 by Beatrice Roethke as Executrix of the Estate of Theodore Roethke, "My Papa's Waltz," © 1942 by Hearst Magazines, Inc., "The Serpent," © 1950 by Theodore Roethke, and "The Sloth," © 1950 by Theodore Roethke. All from *The Collected Poems of Theodore Roethke.* Reprinted by permission of Doubleday & Company, Inc.

(Acknowledgements continued on page 124)

Editorial Director: Joy Zweigler
Cover photographs by Robin Matheny

Contents

Tree into Hand and Foot, drawing by Pavel Tchelitchew. The Museum of Modern Art, New York. Peggy Guggenheim Collection

Two Anglo-Saxon Riddles

1   The wave, over the wave, a weird thing I saw,
    through-wrought, and wonderfully ornate:
    a wonder on the wave — water became bone.

2   Their dark bodies, dun-coated,
        when the breeze bears them up over the backs of the hills
    are black, diminutive.
                        Bold singers,
    they go in companies, call out loudly;
    they tread the timbered cliff, and at times the eaves
    of men's houses.
                    How do they call themselves?

ANONYMOUS Translated from the Anglo-Saxon by Michael Alexander

What Am I?

1   Without a bridle or a saddle,
    Across a thing I ride a-straddle;
    And those I ride, by help of me,
    Though almost blind are made to see.

2   I've seen you where you never were,
    And where you ne'er will be,
    And yet within that self-same place
    You can be seen by me.

TRADITIONAL

School Daze

Certain schools
    Are just big "fiddles,"
Riddled by rules
    And ruled by riddles.

JOHN ROSCOE

Who's Who?

1   Noah of old three babies had,
Or grown-up children, rather;
Shem, Ham, and Japheth, they were called,
Now who was Japheth's father?

2   Brothers and sisters have I none,
But that man's father is my father's son.

3   If Dick's father is John's son,
What relation is Dick to John?

TRADITIONAL

What's Where?

INFIR taris,
Inoak noneis,
Inmud eelsare,
Inclay noneare,
Goatseativy;
Mareseatoats.

TRADITIONAL

A Problem of Commas

I saw a pack of cards gnawing a bone
I saw a dog seated on Britain's throne
I saw the Queen shut up within a box
I saw a shilling driving a fat ox
I saw a man lying in a muff all night
I saw a glove reading news by candle-light
I saw a woman not a twelvemonth old
overcoat   I saw a greatcoat all of solid gold
I saw two buttons telling of their dreams
I heard my friends, who wish'd I'd quit these themes.

TRADITIONAL

What's Going On Here?

Rise up, Don Nippery Septo,
Out of your easy degree!
Put on your sounding crackers,
And your down-treaders.
Call up Dame, Dame Paradise
And your daughter Stride-a-bush,
And come and see!
White faced Similie
Has jumped into hot popolorum
Run up high cockalorum with igniferum on her back
And without absolution we shall all be undone.

TRADITIONAL

A Curious Inscription

P R S V R Y P R F C T M N
V R K P T H S P R C P T S T N

The above letters were affixed to the communion table of a small church in Wales, and continued to puzzle the learned congregation for some centuries. By adding *one* vowel to these consonants can you make sense of it?

A Cockney Alphabet

A	horses	J	oranges	S	you
B	mutton	K	a cuppa	T	two
C	the Highlanders	L	leather	U	mism
D	dumb	M	sis	V	la France
E	brick	N	eggs	W	a pound
F	vescence	O	my dead body	X	breakfast
G	police	P	a penny	Y	girl-friend
H	it	Q	the flicks	Z	his hat
I	looting	R	mo		

TRADITIONAL

A Portrait of the Foot

At the top of crossed foot branches
two rows of bunches
of small, fat birds are hunched.
Somehow they manage to touch

with tenderness. Short,
bundled up, squat
peasants,
they begin to dance.

JOHN LOGAN

Jabberwocky

'Twas brillig, and the slithy toves
    Did gyre and gimble in the wabe;
All mimsy were the borogoves,
    And the mome raths outgrabe.

"Beware the Jabberwock, my son!
    The jaws that bite, the claws that catch!
Beware the Jubjub bird, and shun
    The frumious Bandersnatch!"

He took his vorpal sword in hand:
    Long time the manxome foe he sought —
So rested he by the Tumtum tree,
    And stood awhile in thought.

And as in uffish thought he stood,
    The Jabberwock, with eyes of flame,
Came whiffling through the tulgey wood,
    And burbled as it came!

One, two! One, two! And through and through
    The vorpal blade went snicker-snack!
He left it dead, and with its head
    He went galumphing back.

"And hast thou slain the Jabberwock?
    Come to my arms, my beamish boy!
O frabjous day! Callooh! Callay!"
    He chortled in his joy.

'Twas brillig, and the slithy toves
    Did gyre and gimble in the wabe;
All mimsy were the borogoves,
    And the mome raths outgrabe.

"You seem very clever at explaining words, Sir," said Alice. "Would you kindly tell me the meaning of the poem called 'Jabberwocky'?"

"Let's hear it," said Humpty Dumpty. "I can explain all the poems that ever were invented — and a good many that haven't been invented just yet."

This sounded very hopeful, so Alice repeated the first verse:

'Twas brillig, and the slithy toves
Did gyre and gimble in the wabe;
All mimsy were the borogoves,
And the mome raths outgrabe.

"That's enough to begin with," Humpty Dumpty interrupted: "there are plenty of hard words there. '*Brillig*' means four o'clock in the afternoon — the time when you begin *broiling* things for dinner."

"That'll do very well," said Alice: "and '*slithy*'?"

"Well, '*slithy*' means 'lithe and slimy.' 'Lithe' is the same as 'active.' You see it's like a portmanteau — there are two meanings packed up into one word."

"I see it now," Alice remarked thoughtfully: "and what are '*toves*'?"

"Well, '*toves*' are something like badgers — they're something like lizards — and they're something like corkscrews."

"They must be very curious-looking creatures."

"They are that," said Humpty Dumpty: "also they make their nests under sun-dials — also they live on cheese."

"And what's to '*gyre*' and to '*gimble*'?"

"To '*gyre*' is to go round and round like a gyroscope. To '*gimble*' is to make holes like a gimlet."

"And '*the wabe*' is the grass-plot round a sun-dial, I suppose?" said Alice, surprised at her own ingenuity.

"Of course it is. It's called '*wabe*,' you know, because it goes a long way before it, and a long way behind it. . . ."

"And a long way beyond it on each side," Alice added.

"Exactly so. Well then, '*mimsy*' is 'flimsy and miserable' (there's another portmanteau for you). And a '*borogove*' is a thin shabby-looking bird with its feathers sticking out all round — something like a live mop."

And then '*mome raths*'?" said Alice. "I'm afraid I'm giving you a great deal of trouble."

"Well, a '*rath*' is a sort of green pig: but '*mome*' I'm not certain about. I think it's short for 'from home' — meaning that they'd lost their way, you know."

"And what does '*outgrabe*' mean?"

"Well, '*outgribing*' is something between bellowing and whistling, with a kind of sneeze in the middle: however, you'll hear it done, maybe — down in the wood yonder — and, when you've once heard it, you'll be *quite* content. Who's been repeating all that hard stuff to you?"

"I read it in a book," said Alice. "But I had some poetry repeated to me much easier than that, by — Tweedledee, I think it was."

"As to poetry, you know," said Humpty Dumpty, stretching out one of his great hands, "*I* can repeat poetry as well as other folk, if it comes to that —"

"Oh, it needn't come to that!" Alice hastily said, hoping to keep him from beginning.

LEWIS CARROLL

Word Counts

1   ONE-ERY, two-ery, tickery, seven,
Hallibo, crackibo, ten and eleven,
Spin, span, muskidan,
Twiddle-um, twaddle-um, twenty-one.

2   ONE-ERUM, two-erum,
Cockerum, shu-erum,
Shetherum, shatherum,
Wineberry, wagtail,
Tarrydiddle, den.

TRADITIONAL

Counting-Out Rhyme

Silver bark of beech, and sallow
Bark of yellow birch and yellow
    Twig of willow.

Stripe of green in moosewood maple,
Colour seen in leaf of apple,
    Bark of popple.

Wood of popple pale as moonbeam,
Wood of oak for yoke and barn-beam,
    Wood of hornbeam.

Silver bark of beech, and hollow
Stem of elder, tall and yellow
    Twig of willow.

EDNA ST. VINCENT MILLAY

Twelve Tongue Twisters

One old Oxford ox opening oysters.
Two toads totally tired trying to trot to Tisbury.
Three thick thumping tigers taking toast for tea.
Four finicky fishermen fishing for finny fish.
Five frippery Frenchmen foolishly fishing for frogs.
Six sportsmen shooting snipe.
Seven Severn salmon swallowing shrimps.
Eight eminent Englishmen eagerly examining Europe.
Nine nimble noblemen nibbling nectarines.
Ten tinkering tinkers tinkering ten tin tinder-boxes.
Eleven elephants elegantly equipped.
Twelve typographical topographers typically translating types.

TRADITIONAL

Ululation

With a bray, with a yap,
with a grunt, snort, neigh,
with a growl, bark, yelp,
with a buzz, hiss, howl,
with a chirrup, mew, moo,
with a snarl, baa, wail,
with a blatter, hoot, bay,
with a screech, drone, yowl,
with a cackle, gaggle, guggle,
with a chuck, cluck, clack,
with a hum, gobble, quack,
with a roar, blare, bellow,
with a yip, croak, crow,
with a whinny, caw, low,
with a bleat, with a cheep, with a squawk, with a squeak:
animals
      — and sometimes humans —
                      speak!

EVE MERRIAM

Child's Bouncing Song

Molly Vickers
wets her knickers,
Georgie's father's big and black,
cream on Sunday
milk on Monday,
I'm the cock of all the back.

king, back yard

Tell me who's a
bigger boozer
Mister Baker beats them all,
truck   from his lorry
watch him hurry,
touch the ground and touch the wall.

Who're the gentry
down our entry —
Mrs Smith's got two T.V.'s.
What if her coat
is a fur coat,
all her kids are full of fleas.

Joan loves Harry,
Jack will marry
Edna when they both grow up,
I'll announce it,
bounce bounce bounce it,
our dog Whisker's had a pup.

High and low and
to and fro and
down the street and up the hill,
Mrs Cuthbert's
died   husband snuffed it,
she got nothing from his will.

Mister, mister,
Shirley's sister
at the seaside   won a prize on Blackpool prom,
mam'll smother
our kid brother
truant officers   when the school inspectors come.

Skip and hopping
I'm off shopping,
Tuesday night it's pie for tea,
please to take this
ball and make this
song of bouncing song for me.

TONY CONNOR

Counting

If you get tired of counting *one, two, three,* make up your own numbers, as shepherds used to do when they had to count sheep day in, day out. You can try using these sets of words instead of numbers when you have to count to ten.

Ounce	Instant	Archery
Dice	Distant	Butchery
Trice	Tryst	Treachery
Quartz	Catalyst	Taproom
Quince	Quest	Tomb
Sago	Sycamore	Sermon
Serpent	Sophomore	Cinnamon
Oxygen	Oculist	Apron
Nitrogen	Novelist	Nunnery
Denim	Dentist	Density

ALASTAIR REID

Counting One to Twenty

Yahn, Tayn, Tether, Mether, Mumph,
Hither, Lither, Auver, Dauver, Dic,
Yahndic, Tayndic, Tetherdic,
        Metherdic, Mumphit,
Yahn a mumphit, Tayn a mumphit,
Tethera mumphit, Methera mumphit,
        Jig it.

TRADITIONAL

The Computer's First Christmas Card

jollymerry
hollyberry
jollyberry
merryholly
happyjolly
jollyjelly
jellybelly
bellymerry
hollyheppy
jollyMolly
marryJerry
merryHarry
hoppyBarry
heppyJarry
boppyheppy
berryjorry
jorryjolly
moppyjelly
Mollymerry
Jerryjolly
bellyboppy
jorryhoppy
hollymoppy
Barrymerry
Jarryhappy
happyboppy
boppyjolly
jollymerry
merrymerry
merrymerry
merryChris
ammerryasa
Chrismerry
aSMERRYCHR
YSANTHEMUM

EDWIN MORGAN

l(a

le
af
fa

ll

s)
one
l

iness

E. E. CUMMINGS

n
OthI
n

g can

s
urPas
s

the m

y
SteR
y

of

s
tilLnes
s

E. E. CUMMINGS

The Old Man's Song

I have grown old,
I have lived much,
Many things I understand,
But four riddles I cannot solve.
Ha-ya-ya-ya.

The sun's origin,
The moon's nature,
The minds of women,
And why people have so many lice.
Ha-ya-ya-ya.

ANONYMOUS Translated from the Eskimo by Peter Freuchen

The Little Cart

The little cart jolting and banging through the yellow haze of dusk.
    The man pushing behind: the woman pulling in front.
They have left the city and do not know where to go.
"Green, green, those elm-tree leaves: *they* will cure my hunger,
    If only we could find some quiet place and sup on them together."

    The wind has flattened the yellow mother-wort:
    Above it in the distance they see the walls of a house.
"*There* surely must be people living who'll give you something to
    eat."
They tap at the door, but no one comes: they look in, but the
    kitchen is empty.
They stand hesitating in the lonely road and their tears fall like rain.

CH'EN TSU-LUNG Translated from the Chinese by Arthur Waley

My Uncle Jack

My Uncle Jack collects door knobs;
Door knobs here, door knobs there
Door knobs simply everywhere;
Six on the window, twelve on the door
There's hardly room for any more;
Door knobs on the light switch and on the wall,
My Uncle Jack has got them all;
Blue ones, green ones, yellow ones and red
And a row of gray ones on the bottom of his bed.

DAVID AMEY Age 10 England

My Papa's Waltz

The whiskey on your breath
Could make a small boy dizzy;
But I hung on like death:
Such waltzing was not easy.

We romped until the pans
Slid from the kitchen shelf;
My mother's countenance
Could not unfrown itself.

The hand that held my wrist
Was battered on one knuckle;
At every step you missed
My right ear scraped a buckle.

You beat time on my head
With a palm caked hard by dirt,
Then waltzed me off to bed
Still clinging to your shirt.

THEODORE ROETHKE

Buffalo Bill's

Buffalo Bill's
defunct
        who used to
        ride a watersmooth-silver
                                stallion
and break onetwothreefourfive pigeonsjustlikethat
                                        Jesus
he was a handsome man
                        and what i want to know is
how do you like your blueeyed boy
Mister Death

E. E. CUMMINGS

Dreams

Hold fast to dreams
For if dreams die
Life is a broken-winged bird
That cannot fly.

Hold fast to dreams
For when dreams go
Life is a barren field
Frozen with snow.

LANGSTON HUGHES

Epitaph on a "Marf"

mouth   Wot a marf 'e'd got,
Wot a marf.
When 'e was a kid,
Goo' Lor' luv'll
'Is pore old muvver
Must 'a' fed 'im wiv a shuvvle.

Wot a gap 'e'd got,
Pore chap,
'E'd never been known to larf,
'Cos if 'e did
pound   It's a penny to a quid
'E'd 'a' split 'is fice in 'arf.

TRADITIONAL

Two Epitaphs

JULIA ADAMS,
Died through wearing thin shoes.
April 17th, 1839.
Aged 19 years.

She was not smart, she was not fair,
But hearts with grief for her are swellin';
And empty stands her little chair:
She died of eatin' water melon.

Both of these epitaphs were found on early gravestones in New Jersey.

Another

Here a pretty baby lies
Sung asleep with lullabies:
Pray be silent and not stir
Th' easy earth that covers her.

ROBERT HERRICK

Tall Tales

1   What is the difference between a warder and a jeweller?

2   What is the difference between a big black cloud and
    a lion with a toothache?

3   What is the difference between an angry circus owner
    and a Roman hairdresser?

4   Why did the viper vipe 'er nose?

5   What did the ear 'ear?

6   Why did the moonbeam?

7   Can the orange box?

8   What did Noah say when he heard the rain come down?

9   What would Neptune say if the sea dried up?

10   There was a man in a house and he could not get out.
    The only furniture was a table. He rubbed his hands
    until they were sore. Then he sawed the table in half.
    Two halves make a whole. He shouted through the hole
    until he was hoarse, jumped on the horse and rode away.

    TRADITIONAL

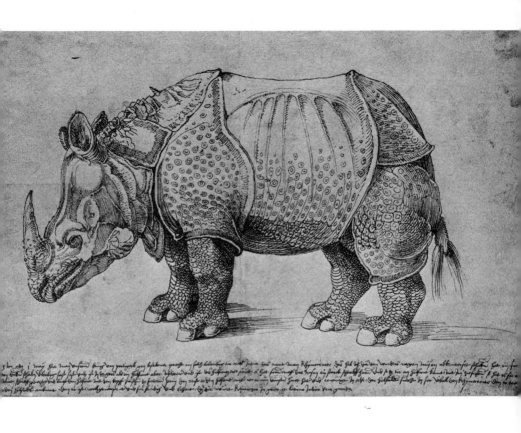

The Derby Ram

As I was going to Derby, sir,
Upon a market day,
I saw the biggest ram, sir,
That ever was fed on hay.

And indeed, sir, 'tis true, sir,
I never was given to lie
And if you'd been to Derby, sir,
You'd have seen him as well as I.

This ram was fat behind, sir,
This ram was fat before.
He measured ten yards round, sir,
If not a little more.

He had four feet to walk on, sir,
He had four feet to stand,
And every foot he had, sir,
Did cover an acre of land.

The man who killed this ram, sir,
Was drowned in all the blood,
And he who held the dish, sir,
Was carried away in the flood.

The mutton that ram made, sir,
Gave all the Army meat,
And what was left, I'm told, sir,
Was served out to the Fleet.

The wool grew on his back, sir,
It reached up to the sky,
And there the eagles built their nests,
I heard the young ones cry.

The wool grew on his belly, sir,
It reached down to the ground,
And that was sold in Derby town
For forty thousand pound.

The horns upon this ram, sir,
They reached up to the moon.
A little boy went up in January
And he never got back till June.

And all the boys of Derby
Came begging for his eyes,
To make themselves some footballs,
For they were of football size.

TRADITIONAL

Daniel

INSCRIBED TO ISADOR BENNETT REED

Beginning with a
strain of "Dixie"

Darius the Mede was a king and a wonder.
His eye was proud, and his voice was thunder.
He kept bad lions in a monstrous den.
He fed up the lions on Christian men.

With a touch of
"Alexander's
Ragtime Band"

Daniel was the chief hired man of the land.
He stirred up the music in the palace band.
He whitwashed the cellar. He shovelled in the coal.
And Daniel kept a-praying: — "Lord save my soul."
Daniel kept a-praying: — "Lord save my soul."
Daniel kept a-praying: — "Lord save my soul."

Daniel was the butler, swagger and swell.
He ran up stairs. He answered the bell.
And *he* would let in whoever came a-calling: —
Saints so holy, scamps so appalling.
"Old man Ahab leaves his card.
Elisha and the bears are a-waiting in the yard.
Here comes Pharaoh and his snakes a-calling.
Here comes Cain and his wife a-calling.
Shadrach, Meshach and Abednego for tea.
Here comes Jonah and the whale,
And the *Sea!*
Here comes St Peter and his fishing pole.
Here comes Judas and his silver a-calling.
Here comes old Beelzebub a-calling."
And Daniel kept a-praying: — "Lord save my soul."
Daniel kept a-praying: — "Lord save my soul."
Daniel kept a-praying: — "Lord save my soul."

His sweetheart and his mother were Christian and
    meek.
They washed and ironed for Darius every week.
One Thursday he met them at the door: —
Paid them as usual, but acted sore.

He said: — "Your Daniel is a dead little pigeon.
He's a good hard worker, but he talks religion."
And he showed them Daniel in the lion's cage.
Daniel standing quietly, the lions in a rage.
His good old mother cried: —
"Lord save him."
And Daniel's tender sweetheart cried: —
"Lord save him."

This to be repeated
three times, very
softly and slowly And she was a golden lily in the dew.
And she was as sweet as an apple on the tree
And she was as fine as a melon in the corn-field,
Gliding and lovely as a ship on the sea,
Gliding and lovely as a ship on the sea.

And she prayed to the Lord: —
"Send Gabriel. Send Gabriel."

King Darius said to the lions: —
"Bite Daniel. Bite Daniel.
Bite him. Bite him. Bite him!"

Here the audience
roars with the
leader Thus roared the lions: —
"We want Daniel, Daniel, Daniel,
We want Daniel, Daniel, Daniel.
Grrrrrrrrrrrrrrrrrrrrr rrrrrrrrrrrrrrrrrrr
Grrrrrrrrrrrrrrrrrrrrr rrrrrrrrrrrrrrrrrrrrr."

And Daniel did not frown.
Daniel did not cry.
He kept on looking at the sky.
And the Lord said to Gabriel: —
The audience
sings this with the
leader, to the old
Negro tune "Go chain the lions down,
Go chain the lions down.
Go chain the lions down.
Go chain the lions down."

And Gabriel chained the lions,
And Gabriel chained the lions,

And Gabriel chained the lions,
And Daniel got out of the den,
And Daniel got out of the den,
And Daniel got out of the den.
And Darius said: — "You're a Christian child,"
Darius said: — "You're a Christian child,"
Darius said: — "You're a Christian child,"
And gave him his job again,
And gave him his job again,
And gave him his job again.

VACHEL LINDSAY

The Weekly Sunday School

Jonah was an emigrant, so says the Bible tale,
Who booked himself a passage in a transatlantic whale;
But Jonah in the bowels of the whale was sore oppressed
So he simply pressed the button, and the whale he did the rest.

Old folks, young folks, everybody come
To the weekly Sunday school and make yourselves at home.
Check your sticks of chewing gum and razors at the door
And we'll tell you Bible stories that you've never heard before.

Adam was the first bloke that ever got invented,
And though he lived for all his life, he never was contented;
He was fashioned out of mud pies in the distant days gone by,
And then they pegged him on the line in the sunshine to get dry.

Esau was a cowboy in the wild and woolly West,
His father left him half the farm, and brother Jake the rest;
But Esau saw the title-deeds was anything but clear
So he sold them to his brother for a sandwich and a beer.

Old Noah was a mariner, who sailed across the sea,
With half a dozen boys and girls and a big menagerie;
They all went stoney-broke because it rained for forty days
And in that kind of weather ne'er a circus never pays.

Elijah was a prophet who appeared at wakes and fairs,
And advertised his business with a pair of dancing bears;
He used to sell his prophecies on Sat'day afternoon
And went up in the evening in a painted fire balloon.

David was a shepherd and a weedy little chap,
And along came Big Goliath who was dying for a scrap;
Now David didn't want to fight, but thought he must or bust,
half- So he picked up some half-enders and busted in his crust.
bricks

Samson was a pugilist and just as green as grass;
He slew ten thousand Philistines with the jawbone of an ass.
But when Delilah captured him, she filled him up with gin,
police- Shaved his hair clean off his head, and the bobbies ran him in.
men

Now Joseph was put down a well because he wouldn't work,
He lost his pretty rainbow coat because he'd rather shirk;
wept He bellowed, bawled and blarted far into the night
But of course you couldn't see him, seeing he was out of sight.

Well then a great big caravan was coming past the place,
It was loaded down with frankincense and imitation lace.
They heard poor Joseph yelling and they pulled him out of
        the well;
If you don't like my conclusion, well then, you can go to Hell.

TRADITIONAL

Brian O Linn

Brian O Linn had no breeches to wear,
He got an old sheepskin to make him a pair.
With the fleshy side out and the woolly side in,
"They'll be pleasant and cool," says Brian O Linn.

Brian O Linn had no shirt to his back,
He went to a neighbor's, and borrowed a sack,
Then he puckered the meal bag in under his chin —
"Sure they'll take them for ruffles," says Brian O Linn.

Brian O Linn was hard up for a coat,
So he borrowed the skin of a neighboring goat,
armpits With the horns sticking out from his oxsters, and then,
"Sure they'll take them for pistols," says Brian O Linn.

Brian O Linn had no hat to put on,
So he got an old beaver to make him a one,
There was none of the crown left and less of the brim,
"Sure there's fine ventilation," says Brian O Linn.

shoes Brian O Linn had no brogues for his toes,
He hopped in two crab-shells to serve him for those.
Then he split up two oysters that match'd like a twin,
"Sure they'll shine out like buckles," says Brian O Linn.

Brian O Linn had no watch to put on,
So he scooped out a turnip to make him a one.
Then he placed a young cricket in-under the skin —
"Sure they'll think it is ticking," says Brian O Linn.

Brian O Linn to his house had no door,
He'd the sky for a roof, and the bog for a floor;
He'd a way to jump out, and a way to swim in,
"'Tis a fine habitation," says Brian O Linn.

TRADITIONAL

The Housewife's Lament

One day I was walking, I heard a complaining
And saw an old woman the picture of gloom.
She gazed at the mud on her doorstep, 'twas raining,
And this was her song as she wielded her broom.

 O life is a toil, and love is a trouble.
 Beauty will fade and riches will flee.
 Pleasures they dwindle and prices they double
 And nothing is as I would wish it to be.

There's too much of worriment goes to a bonnet,
There's too much of ironing goes to a shirt,
There's nothing that pays for the time that you waste on it,
There's nothing that lasts but trouble and dirt.

In March it is mud, it is slush in December,
The midsummer breezes are loaded with dust.
In fall the leaves litter, in muddy September
The wallpaper rots and the candlesticks rust.

It's sweeping at six and it's dusting at seven.
dinner It's victuals at eight and it's dishes at nine.
It's potting and panning from ten to eleven.
We've scarce finished breakfast, we're ready to dine.

Last night in my dreams I was stationed forever
On a far little rock in the midst of the sea.
effort My one chance of life was a ceaseless endeavor
To sweep off the waves as they swept over me.

Alas! 'Twas no dream; ahead I behold it,
I see I am helpless my fate to avert.
She lay down her broom, her apron she folded,
She lay down and died, and was buried in dirt.

TRADITIONAL

Wonder Wander

in the afternoon the children walk like ducks
like geese
like from here to there
eyeing bird-trees puppy dogs candy windows
sun balls ice cream wagons
lady bugs rose bushes fenced yards vacant lots
tall buildings
and other things
big business men take big business walks
wear big business clothes
carry big business briefcases talk about
big business affairs in
big business voices
young girls walk pretty on the streets
stroll the avenues linger by
shop windows wedding rings lady hats
shiny dresses fancy shoes
whisper like turkey hens passing the time
young men stride on parade dream headed
wild eyed eating up the world
with deep glances rubbing empty fingers
in their empty pockets and
planning
me, I wander around soft-shoed easy-legged
watching the scene as it goes
finding things sea-gull feathers pink baby roses
everytime I see a letter on the sidewalk
I stop and look it might be
        for me

LENORE KANDEL

Children's Games

Little girls
whirling their skirts about
until they stand out flat

tops pinwheels
to run in the wind with
or a toy in 3 tiers to spin

with a piece
of twine to make it go
blindman's-buff follow the

leader stilts
high and low tipcat jacks
bowls hanging by the knees

standing on your head
run the gauntlet
a dozen on their backs

feet together kicking
through which a boy must pass
roll the hoop or a

construction
made of bricks
some mason has abandoned

WILLIAM CARLOS WILLIAMS

Children's Games

The desperate toys
of children
their

balance   imagination equilibrium
and rocks
which are to be

found
everywhere
and games to drag

the other down
blindfold
to make use of

a swinging
weight
with which

at random
to bash in the
heads about

them
Brueghel saw it all
and with his grim

humor faithfully
recorded
it

WILLIAM CARLOS WILLIAMS

The Two Witches

O sixteen hundred and ninety-one,
Never was year so well begun,
Backsy-forsy and inside out,
The best of years to ballad about.

On the first fine day of January
I ran to my sweetheart Margery
And tossed her over the roof so far
That down she fell like a shooting star.

But when we two had frolicked and kissed
She clapped her fingers about my wrist
And tossed me over the chimney stack,
And danced on me till my bones did crack.

Then, when she had labored to ease my pain,
We sat by the stile of Robin's Lane,
She in a hare and I in a toad
And puffed at the clouds till merry they glowed.

We spelled our loves until close of day.
I wished her good-night and walked away,
But she put out a tongue that was long and red
And swallowed me down like a crumb of bread.

ROBERT GRAVES

The Sioux Indians

I'll sing you a song and it'll be a sad one,
Of trials and troubles and how first begun,
We left our dear kindred, our friends and our home,
Across the wild deserts and mountains to roam. (*twice*)

We crossed the Missouri and joined a large train,
Which bore us o'er mountains and valleys and plains,
And often of an evening out hunting we'd go
To shoot the fleet antelope and the wild buffalo. (*twice*)

We heard of Sioux Indians all out on the plains,
A-killing poor drivers and burning their trains,
A-killing poor drivers with arrows and bows,
When captured by Indians, no mercy they'd show. (*twice*)

We travelled three weeks till we came to the Platte,
We set up our camp at the head of the flat,
We spread down our blankets on the green, grassy ground,
While our mules and our horses were grazing around. (*twice*)

While taking refreshment we heard a low yell,
The whoop of Sioux Indians coming out of the dell,
We sprang to our rifles with a flash in each eye,
"Boys," said our brave leader, "we'll fight till we die." (*twice*)

They made a bold dash and come near to our train,
The arrows fell round us like showers of rain,
But with our long rifles we fed them hot lead,
Till many a brave warrior around us lay dead. (*twice*)

In our little band there were just twenty-four,
And of the Sioux Indians, five hundred or more,
We fought them with courage, we said not a word,
The whoop of the Indians was all could be heard. (*twice*)

We shot their bold chief at the head of his band.
He died like a warrior with his bow in his hand,
When they saw their brave chief lying dead in his gore,
They whooped and they yelled and we saw them no more. (*twice*)

We travelled by day, guarded camp in the night,
Till Oregon's mountains look'd high in their might,
Now in a green valley, beside a clear stream,
Our journey has ended in the land of our dream. (*twice*)

TRADITIONAL

What's What?

Most people know
the story of how
the frog was a prince
and the dragon was ticklish,
or how the princess
grew fat in the end;
nevertheless,
think of the chance
that the youngest son took —
gloom to the left of him,
groans to the right of him,
no spell to tell him
which way to take,
no map, no book,
no real interest.
All he could say was
"maybe I'm me,"
but he knew not to trust
the wizards who seemed,
the bird with the breast
of too many colors,
the princess who hummed
too perfect a song.
The going was not good,
but his curious head
said over and over
ridiculous words
like *quince* and *Fray Bentos*
all through the wood.
"Yes," he said firmly,
"nobody pays me,
nobody knows me,
so I will decide
which tree will amaze me
when I see a leaf
I can be sure of.
Whom do I listen to?
Not that toad
with the gem in its head,
nor that mole that mumbles

precise directions,
nor the nice wizard,
so soft and helpful,
nor sweet old women

firewood gathering faggots.
It's that clumsy bird
who looks away,
with only one eye —
untidy feathers,
flying absent-mindedly,
out in all weathers,
little to say —
he's for me.
He's not after
a cut of the treasure.
He knows well
that he's going nowhere
and, what's more,
he doesn't care.

If I'd listened to wizards
and looked in crystals,
I'd be expert
at going wrong;
but I know my birdsong.
Hearing his *tip-tippy*,
I know who *he* is.
I'll go *his* way."

Needless to say,
the youngest son won
with enough to go on;
and the one-eyed bird,
whoever he was,
went *tip-tip-tippy*
to pleasure his own
well-worn feathers,
over and over,
with no one to hear . . .

Then, one day,
the youngest son
had a youngest son,
and so on.

ALASTAIR REID

I Wish That My Room Had a Floor

I wish that my room had a floor!
I don't so much care for a door,
  But this crawling around
  Without touching the ground
Is getting to be quite a bore!

GELETT BURGESS

The Doors

The doors in my house
Are used every day
For closing rooms
And locking children away.

BRIAN ANDREWS Age 10 Australia

Digging for China

"Far enough down is China," somebody said.
"Dig deep enough and you might see the sky
  As clear as at the bottom of a well.
  Except it would be real — a different sky.
  Then you could burrow down until you came
  To China! Oh, it's nothing like New Jersey.
  There's people, trees, and houses, and all that,
  But much, much different. Nothing looks the same."

I went and got the trowel out of the shed
And sweated like a coolie all that morning,
Digging a hole beside the lilac-bush,
Down on my hands and knees. It was a sort
Of praying, I suspect. I watched my hand
Dig deep and darker, and I tried and tried
To dream a place where nothing was the same.
The trowel never did break through to blue.

Before the dream could weary of itself
My eyes were tired of looking into darkness,
My sunbaked head of hanging down a hole.
I stood up in a place I had forgotten,
Blinking and staggering while the earth went round
And showed me silver barns, the fields dozing
In palls of brightness, patens growing and gone
In the tides of leaves, and the whole sky china blue.
Until I got my balance back again
All that I saw was China, China, China.

dishes *or* plates

RICHARD WILBUR

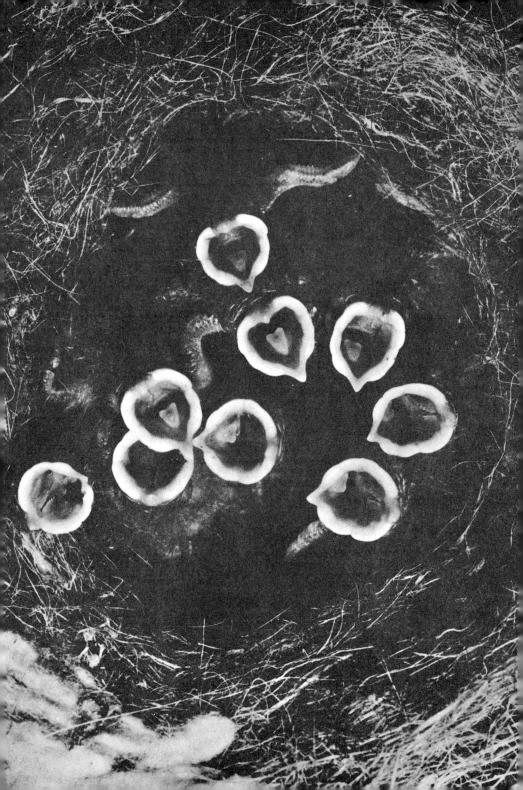

Holes

One day
My mother yawned, her
Mouth an out and outstretched
Hole.
Keeping my feet firmly on the ground,
I peered in.
Almost fell, in.

Look, said the clown,
Your nose has two holes in it.
For every word mouth speaks,
Nose utters two,
Siamese sniffs and snores.

He talks and talks,
Building a wall of words.
I take my muted trumpet
And silently blow, blow, blow
Out, through his word-wall.
Still, my, head, nods,
Politely, thinking miles away.
And still he talks and talks,
Certain-sure that I'm still, still,
Inside his Jericho, ericho, ericho, ericho.

JUSTIN ST. JOHN

My Father

Some fathers work at the office, others work at the store,
Some operate great cranes and build up skyscrapers galore,
Some work in canning factories counting green peas into cans,
Some drive all night in huge and thundering removal vans.
But mine has the strangest job of the lot.
My father's the Chief Inspector of — What?
O don't tell the mice, don't tell the moles,
My Father's the Chief Inspector of HOLES.

moving
vans

It's a work of the highest importance because you never know
What's in a hole, what fearful thing is creeping from below.
Perhaps it's a hole to the ocean and will soon gush water in tons,
Or maybe it leads to a vast cave full of gold and skeletons.

Though a hole might seem to have nothing but dirt in,
Somebody's simply got to make certain.
Caves in the mountain, clefts in the wall,
My Father has to inspect them all.

That crack in the road looks harmless. My Father knows it's not.
The world may be breaking into two and starting at that spot.
Or maybe the world is a great egg, and we live on the shell,
And it's just beginning to split and hatch: you simply cannot
tell.

If you see a crack, run to the phone, run;
My Father will know just what's to be done.
A rumbling hole, a silent hole,
My Father will soon have it under control.

Keeping a check on all these holes he hurries from morning to
night.
There might be sounds of marching in one, or an eye shining
bright.
A tentacle came groping from a hole that belonged to a mouse,
A floor collapsed and Chinamen swarmed up into the house.

A Hole's an unpredictable thing —
Nobody knows what a Hole might bring.
Caves in the mountain, clefts in the wall,
My Father has to inspect them all!

TED HUGHES

The Ballad of Rudolph Reed

Rudolph Reed was oaken.
His wife was oaken too.
And his two good girls and his good little man
Oakened as they grew.

"I am not hungry for berries.
I am not hungry for bread.
But hungry hungry for a house
Where at night a man in bed

"May never hear the plaster
Stir as if in pain.
May never hear the roaches
Falling like fat rain.

"Where never wife and children need
Go blinking through the gloom.
Where every room of many rooms
Will be full of room.

"Oh my home may have its east or west
Or north or south behind it.
All I know is I shall know it,
And fight for it when I find it."

It was in a street of bitter white.
That he made his application.
For Rudolph Reed was oakener
Than others in the nation.

The agent's steep and steady stare
Corroded to a grin.
Why, you black old, tough old hell of a man,
Move your family in!

Nary a grin grinned Rudolph Reed,
Nary a curse cursed he,
But moved in his House. With his dark little wife,
And his dark little children three.

A neighbor would *look,* with a yawning eye
That squeezed into a slit.
But the Rudolph Reeds and the children three
Were too joyous to notice it.

For were they not firm in a home of their own
With windows everywhere
And a beautiful banistered stair
And a front yard for flowers and a back yard for grass?

The first night, a rock, big as two fists.
The second, a rock big as three.
But nary a curse cursed Rudolph Reed.
(Though oaken as man could be.)

The third night, a silvery ring of glass.
Patience ached to endure.
But he looked, and lo! small Mabel's blood
Was staining her gaze so pure.

Then up did rise our Rudolph Reed
And pressed the hand of his wife,
And went to the door with a thirty-four
And a beastly butcher knife.

He ran like a mad thing into the night.
And the words in his mouth were stinking.
By the time he had hurt his first white man
He was no longer thinking.

By the time he had hurt his fourth white man
Rudolph Reed was dead.
His neighbors gathered and kicked his corpse.
"Nigger — " his neighbors said.

Small Mabel whimpered all night long,
For calling herself the cause.
Her oak-eyed mother did no thing
But change the bloody gauze.

GWENDOLYN BROOKS

The Streets of Laredo

As I walked out in the streets of Laredo,
As I walked out in Laredo one day,
I spied a young cowboy all wrapped in white linen,
All wrapped in white linen as cold as the clay.

"I see by your outfit that you are a cowboy" —
These words he did say as I boldly stepped by,
"Come sit down beside me and hear my sad story;
I'm shot in the breast and I know I must die.

"It was once in the saddle I used to go dashing,
Once in the saddle I used to go gay;
First to the ale-house and then to the jail-house,
Got shot in the breast and I'm dying today.

"Get six jolly cowboys to carry my coffin;
Get six pretty maidens to carry my pall;
Put bunches of roses all over my coffin,
Roses to deaden the clods as they fall.

"Oh, beat the drum slowly and play the fife lowly,
Play the dead march as you carry me along;
Take me to the green valley and lay the sod o'er me,
For I'm a young cowboy and I know I've done wrong.

"Go gather around you a crowd of young cowboys
And tell them the story of this, my sad fate;
Tell one and the other before they go further
To stop their wild roving before it's too late.

"Go fetch me a cup, a cup of cold water
To cool my parched lips," the cowboy then said.
Before I returned, the spirit had left him
And gone to its Maker — the cowboy was dead.

We beat the drum slowly and played the fife lowly,
And bitterly wept as we carried him along;
For we all loved our comrade, so brave, young and handsome,
We all loved our comrade although he'd done wrong.

AMERICAN BALLAD

Roll a Rock Down

Oh, out in the West where the riders are ready,
    They sing an old song and they tell an old tale,
And its moral is plain: Take it easy, go steady,
    While riding a horse on the Malibu Trail.

It's a high, rocky trail with its switch-backs and doubles,
    It has no beginning and never an end:
It's risky and rough and it's plumb full of troubles,
    From Shifty — that's shale — up to Powder Cut Bend.

Old-timers will tell you the rangers who made it,
    Sang "Roll a Rock Down," with a stiff upper lip,
And cussed all creation, but managed to grade it;
    With a thousand-foot drop if a pony should slip.

Oh, the day it was wet and the sky it was cloudy,
    The trail was as slick as an oil-rigger's pants,
When Ranger McCabe on his pony, Old Rowdy,
    Came ridin' where walkin' was takin' a chance.

"Oh, Roll a Rock Down!" picks and shovels was clangin',
    And Rowdy a steppin' careful and light,
When the edge it gave way and McCabe was left hangin'
    Clean over the rim — with no bottom in sight.

I shook out a loop — bein' crowded for throwin';
  I flipped a fair noose for a rope that was wet:
It caught just as Mac lost his holt and was goin',
  And burned through my fingers: it's burnin' them yet.

For Ranger McCabe never knuckled to danger;
  My partner in camp, on the trail, or in town:
And he slid into glory, a true forest-ranger,
  With: "Hell! I'm a-goin'! Just roll a rock down."

So, roll a rock down where a ranger is sleepin'
  Aside of his horse below Powder Cut Bend:
I ride and I look where the shadows are creepin',
  And roll a rock down — for McCabe was my friend.

I've sung you my song and I've told you my story,
  And all that I ask when I'm done with the show,
Is, roll a rock down when I slide into glory,
  And say that I went like a ranger should go.

HENRY HERBERT KNIBBS

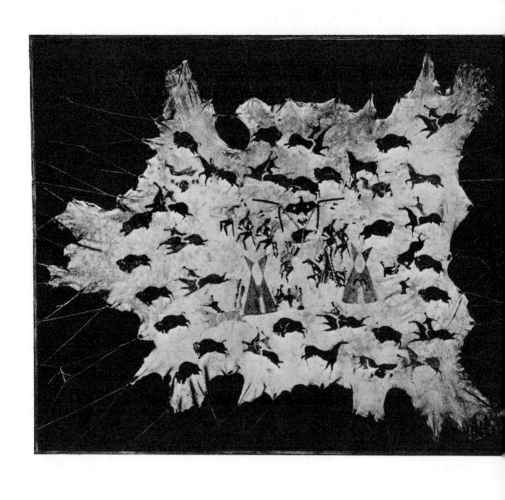

The Rising of the Buffalo Men

I rise, I rise,
I, whose tread makes the earth to rumble.

I rise, I rise,
I, in whose thighs there is strength.

I rise, I rise,
I, who whips his back with his tail when in rage.

I rise, I rise,
I, in whose humped shoulder there is power.

I rise, I rise,
I, who shakes his mane when angered.

I rise, I rise,
I, whose horns are sharp and curved.

AMERICAN INDIAN CHANT

Buffalo Dusk

The buffaloes are gone.
And those who saw the buffaloes are gone.
Those who saw the buffaloes by thousands and
   how they pawed the prairie sod into dust
   with their hoofs, their great heads down
   pawing on in a great pageant of dusk,
Those who saw the buffaloes are gone.
And the buffaloes are gone.

CARL SANDBURG

Magic Song

To Be Recited When in Sudden Danger

You earth,
Our great earth!
See, oh see:
All these heaps
Of bleached bones
And wind-dried skeletons!
They crumble in the air,
The mighty world,
The mighty world's
Air!
Bleached bones,
Wind-dried skeleton,
Crumble in the air!
Hey-hey-hey!

ANONYMOUS Translated from the Eskimo by Peter Freuchen

Chant Before Battle

Let fog fill the skies,
let the cloud cover them,
the wind howls high up
to the world away down,
listen! the wind howls
from far away down!

Shuddering the spear
is charging, is flying,
the twin-bladed shark,
and the footsteps hurtling.

O furious the footsteps,
blood-wet the footsteps
bound for the world's brink.

He goes, god of battles,
the stars in his stride
and the moon in his stride —
run, run from the death-blow!

ANONYMOUS Translated from the Maori by Allen Curnow and Roger Oppenheim

Blackfoot Prayer to the Four Directions

To the West:
Over there are the mountains.
May you see them as long as you live,
for from them you must receive
your sweet pine as incense.

To the North:
Strength will come from the North.
May you look for many years
upon the Star that never moves.

To the East:
Old age will come from below,
where lies the light of the Sun.

To the South:
May the warm winds of the South
bring you success in securing food.

TRADITIONAL

The Base Stealer

Poised between going on and back, pulled
Both ways taut like a tightrope-walker,
Fingertips pointing the opposites,
Now bouncing tiptoe like a dropped ball
Or a kid skipping rope, come on, come on,
Running a scattering of steps sidewise,
How he teeters, skitters, tingles, teases,
Taunts them, hovers like an ecstatic bird,
He's only flirting, crowd him, crowd him,
Delicate, delicate, delicate, delicate — now!

ROBERT FRANCIS

Life Is Motion

In Oklahoma,
Bonnie and Josie,
Dressed in calico,
Danced around a stump.
They cried,
"Ohoyaho,
Ohoo" . . .
Celebrating the marriage
Of flesh and air.

WALLACE STEVENS

Perpetuum Mobile

To all the girls
of all ages
who walk up and down on

the streets of this town
silent or gabbing
putting

their feet down
one before the other
one two

one two they
pause sometimes before
a store window and

reform the line
from here
to China everywhere

back and
forth and back and forth
and back and forth

WILLIAM CARLOS WILLIAMS

The Ups and Downs of the Elevator Car

The elevator car in the elevator shaft,
Complained of the buzzer, complained of the draft.
It said it felt carsick as it rose and fell,
It said it had a headache from the ringing of the bell.

"There is spring in the air," sighed the elevator car.
Said the elevator man, "You are well-off where you are."
The car paid no attention but frowned an ugly frown

```
                          when
              up      it
          going          should
      started                be
       it                      going
 And                             down.
```

Down flashed the signal, but *up* went the car.
The elevator man cried, "You are going much too far!"
Said the elevator car, "I'm doing no such thing.
I'm through with buzzers buzzing. I'm looking for the spring."

Then the elevator man began to shout and call
And all the people came running through the hall.
The elevator man began to call and shout,
"The car won't stop! Let me out! Let me out!"

On went the car past the penthouse door.
On went the car up one flight more.
On went the elevator till it came to the top.
On went the elevator, and it would not stop!

Right through the roof went the man and the car.
And nobody knows where the two of them are!
(Nobody knows but everyone cares,
Wearily, drearily climbing the stairs!)

Now on a summer evening when you see a shooting star
Fly through the air, perhaps it *is* — that elevator car!

CAROLINE C. EMERSON

Foul Shot

With two 60's stuck on the scoreboard
And two seconds hanging on the clock,
The solemn boy in the center of eyes,
Squeezed by silence,
Seeks out the line with his feet,
Soothes his hands along his uniform,
Gently drums the ball against the floor,
Then measures the waiting net,
Raises the ball on his right hand,
Balances it with his left,
Calms it with fingertips,
Breathes,
Crouches,
Waits,
And then through a stretching of stillness,
Nudges it upward.

The ball
Slides up and out,
Lands,
Leans,
Wobbles,
Wavers,
Hesitates,
Exasperates,
Plays it coy
Until every face begs with unsounding screams —

And then

       And then

            And then,

Right before ROAR-UP,
Dives down and through.

EDWIN A. HOEY

The High School Band

On warm days in September the high school band
Is up with the birds and marches along our street,
Boom boom,
To a field where it goes boom boom until eight forty-five
When it marches, as in the old rhyme, back, boom boom,
To its study halls, leaving our street
Empty except for the leaves that descend, to no drum,
And lie still.
In September
A great many high school bands beat a great many drums,
And the silences after their partings are very deep.

REED WHITTEMORE

Depressed by a Book of Bad Poetry, I Walk Toward an Unused Pasture and Invite the Insects To Join Me

Relieved, I let the book fall behind a stone.
I climb a slight rise of grass.
I do not want to disturb the ants
Who are walking single file up the fence post,
Carrying small white petals,
Casting shadows so frail that I can see through them.
I close my eyes for a moment, and listen.
The old grasshoppers
Are tired, they leap heavily now,
Their thighs are burdened.
I want to hear them, they have clear sounds to make.
They have gone to sleep.
Then lovely, far off, a dark cricket begins
In the castles of maple.

JAMES WRIGHT

To Look at Any Thing

To look at any thing,
If you would know that thing,
You must look at it long:
To look at this green and say
"I have seen spring in these
Woods," will not do — you must
Be the thing you see:
You must be the dark snakes of
Stems and ferny plumes of leaves,
You must enter in
To the small silences between
The leaves,
You must take your time
And touch the very peace
They issue from.

JOHN MOFFITT

                              r-p-o-p-h-e-s-s-a-g-r
                    who
        a)s w(e loo)k
        upnowgath
                    PPEGORHRASS
                              eringint(o-

        aThe):l
              eA
                lp:
        S   a
                  (r
        rIvInG   .gRrEaPsPhOs)
                                        to

        rea(be)rran(com)gi(e)ngly
        ,grasshopper;

E. E. CUMMINGS

The Chaffinch Map of Scotland

chaffinch
chaffinchaffinch
chaffinchaffinchaffinch
chaffinchaffinchaffinch
chaffinchaffinch
chaffinch
chaffie   chye   chaffiechaffie
chaffie   chye   chaffiechaffie
chyechaffie
chaffiechaffiechaffie
chaffiechaffiechaffie
chaffiechaffie
chaffiechaffie
chaffiechaffie
chaffiechaffie

shillyshelly
shelfyshilfyshellyshilly
shelfyshillyshilly
shilfyshellyshelly
shilfyshelfyshelly
shellyfaw
shielyshellyfaw
shilfy
shilfyshelfy shielyshiely
shilfyshelfyshelfy   shielychaffie
chaffiechaffie   chaffiechaffie
chaffiechaffie
shilfyshilfyshilfyshelfyshelfy
chaffieshilfyshilfyshelfyshelfyshelfyshelfy
chaffieshilfyshilfyshelfyshelfyshelfyshelfyshelfy
shilfyshilfyshilfyshelfy   shelfyshelfy
shilfy   shilfy
shilfy
shilfyshelfy

brichtie

EDWIN MORGAN

The Dragonfly

The dragonfly:
  his face is very nearly
    only eye!

CHISOKU Translated from the Japanese by Harold G. Henderson

But If . . .

But if I held it . . .
  Could I touch the
  Lightness of this
Flutter-butterfly?

BUSON

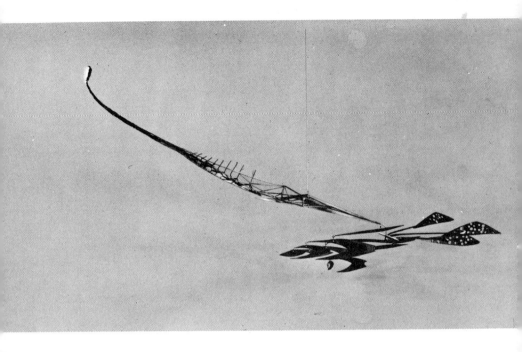

Sounds

Insects one hears —
   and one hears the talk of men —
      with different ears.

WAFU Translated from the Japanese by Harold G. Henderson

Persistence

Did it yell
   till it became *all* voice?
      Cicada-shell!

BASHO Translated from the Japanese by Harold G. Henderson

Pity

Oh, don't mistreat
the fly! He wrings his hands!
He wrings his feet!

ISSA Translated from the Japanese by Harold G. Henderson

Loneliness

At this dreary inn
A hound keeps
Wailing . . . like me
Lonely in the rain?

BASHO

The Wild Geese Leave

Wild geese! I know
that they did eat the barley;
yet, when they go . . .

YASUI Translated from the Japanese by Harold G. Henderson

The Centaur

The summer that I was ten —
Can it be there was only one
summer that I was ten? It must

have been a long one then —
each day I'd go out to choose
a fresh horse from my stable

which was a willow grove
down by the old canal.
I'd go on my two bare feet.

But when, with my brother's jack-knife,
I had cut me a long limber horse
with a good thick knob for a head,

and peeled him slick and clean
except a few leaves for the tail,
and cinched my brother's belt

around his head for a rein,
I'd straddle and canter him fast
up the grass bank to the path,

trot along in the lovely dust
that talcumed over his hoofs,
hiding my toes, and turning

his feet to swift half-moons.
The willow knob with the strap
jouncing between my thighs

was the pommel and yet the poll
of my nickering pony's head.
My head and my neck were mine,

yet they were shaped like a horse.
My hair flopped to the side
like the mane of a horse in the wind.

My forelock swung in my eyes,
my neck arched and I snorted.
I shied and skittered and reared,

stopped and raised my knees,
pawed at the ground and quivered.
My teeth bared as we wheeled

and swished through the dust again.
I was the horse and the rider,
and the leather I slapped to his rump

spanked my own behind.
Doubled, my two hoofs beat
a gallop along the bank,

the wind twanged in my mane,
my mouth squared to the bit.
And yet I sat on my steed

quiet, negligent riding,
my toes standing the stirrups,
my thighs hugging his ribs.

At a walk we drew up to the porch.
I tethered him to a paling.
Dismounting, I smoothed my skirt

and entered the dusky hall.
My feet on the clean linoleum
left ghostly toes in the hall.

Where have you been? said my mother.
Been riding, I said from the sink,
and filled me a glass of water.

What's that in your pocket? she said.
Just my knife. It weighed my pocket
and stretched my dress awry.

Go tie back your hair, said my mother,
and *Why is your mouth all green?*
Rob Roy, he pulled some clover
as we crossed the field, I told her.

MAY SWENSON

Two Songs of a Fool

1   A speckled cat and a tame hare
Eat at my hearthstone
And sleep there;
And both look up to me alone
For learning and defense
As I look up to Providence.

I start out of my sleep to think
Some day I may forget
Their food and drink;
Or, the house door left unshut,
The hare may run till it's found
The horn's sweet note and the tooth of the hound.

I bear a burden that might well try
Men that do all by rule,
And what can I
That am a wandering-witted fool
But pray to God that He ease
My great responsibilities?

2   I slept on my three-legged stool by the fire,
The speckled cat slept on my knee;
We never thought to inquire
Where the brown hare might be,
And whether the door were shut.
Who knows how she drank the wind
Stretched up on two legs from the mat,
Before she had settled her mind
To drum with her heel and to leap?
Had I but awakened from sleep
And called her name, she had heard,
It may be, and had not stirred,
That now, it may be, has found
The horn's sweet note and the tooth of the hound.

W. B. YEATS

The Meadow Mouse

1

In a shoe box stuffed in an old nylon stocking
Sleeps the baby mouse I found in the meadow,
Where he trembled and shook beneath a stick
Till I caught him up by the tail and brought him in,
Cradled in my hand,
A little quaker, the whole body of him trembling,
His absurd whiskers sticking out like a cartoon-mouse,
His feet like small leaves,
Little lizard-feet,
Whitish and spread wide when he tried to struggle away,
Wriggling like a miniscule puppy.

tiny [margin note beside "miniscule"]

Now he's eaten his three kinds of cheese and drunk
        from his bottle-cap watering-trough —
So much he just lies in one corner,
His tail curled under him, his belly big
As his head; his bat-like ears
Twitching, tilting toward the least sound.

Do I imagine he no longer trembles
When I come close to him?
He seems no longer to tremble.

2

But this morning the shoe-box house on the back porch
        is empty.
Where has he gone, my meadow mouse,
My thumb of a child that nuzzled in my palm? —
To run under the hawk's wing,
Under the eye of the great owl watching from the elm-tree,
To live by courtesy of the shrike, the snake, the tom-cat.

I think of the nestling fallen into the deep grass,
The turtle gasping in the dusty rubble of the highway,
The paralyic stunned in the tub, and the water rising, —
All things innocent, hapless, forsaken.

THEODORE ROETHKE

Me up at does

Me up at does

out of the floor
quietly Stare

a poisoned mouse

still who alive

is asking What
have i done that

You wouldn't have

E. E. CUMMINGS

Christopher Smart Considers His Cat, Jeoffry

For I will consider my Cat Jeoffry.

For he is the servant of the Living God, duly and daily serving
him.

For at the first glance of the glory of God in the East he
worships in his way.

For is this done by wreathing his body seven times round with
elegant quickness.

For then he leaps up to catch the musk, which is the blessing
of God upon his prayer.

For he rolls upon prank to work it in.

For having done duty and received blessing he begins to
consider himself.

For this he performs in ten degrees.

For first he looks upon his fore-paws to see if they are clean.

For secondly he kicks up behind to clear away there.

For thirdly he works it upon stretch with the fore-paws
extended.

For fourthly he sharpens his paws by wood.

For fifthly he washes himself.

For sixthly he rolls upon wash.

For seventhly he fleas himself, that he may not be interrupted
upon the beat.

For eighthly he rubs himself against a post.

For ninthly he looks up for his instructions.

For tenthly he goes in quest of food.

For having consider'd God and himself he will consider his
neighbor .

For if he meets another cat he will kiss her in kindness.

For when he takes his prey he plays with it to give it chance.

For one mouse in seven escapes by his dallying.

For when his day's work is done his business more properly
begins.

For he keeps the Lord's watch in the night against the
adversary.

For he counteracts the powers of darkness by his electrical skin
& glaring eyes.

For he counteracts the Devil, who is death, by brisking about
the life.

prayers For in his morning orisons he loves the sun and the sun loves
him.

86

For he is of the tribe of Tiger.

For the Cherub Cat is a term of the Angel Tiger.

For he has the subtlety and hissing of a serpent, which in
goodness he suppresses.

For he will not do destruction, if he is well-fed, neither will he
spit without provocation.

For he purrs in thankfulness, when God tells him he's a good
Cat.

. . . .

For he can fetch and carry, which is patience in employment.

For he can jump over a stick, which is patience upon proof
positive.

For he can spraggle upon waggle at the word of command.

For he can jump from an eminence into his master's bosom.

For he can catch the cork and toss it again.

For he is hated by the hypocrite and miser.

For the former is affraid of detection.

For the latter refuses the charge.

For he camels his back to bear the first notion of business.

For he is good to think on, if a man would express himself
neatly.

For he made a great figure in Egypt for his signal services.

For he killed the Ichneumon-rat very pernicious by land.

For his ears are so acute that they sting again.

For from this proceeds the passing quickness of his attention.

For by stroking of him I have found out electricity.

. . . .

For, tho he cannot fly, he is an excellent clamberer.

For his motions upon the face of the earth are more than any
other quadrupede.

For he can tread to all the measures upon the musick.

For he can swim for life.

For he can creep.

CHRISTOPHER SMART

Egyptian rat that
eats crocodile's
eggs

Catalog

Cats sleep fat and walk thin.
Cats, when they sleep, slump;
When they wake, pull in —
And where the plump's been
There's skin.
Cats walk thin.

Cats wait in a lump,
Jump in a streak.
Cats, when they jump, are sleek
As a grape slipping its skin —
They have technique.
Oh, cats don't creak.
They sneak.

Cats sleep fat.
They spread comfort beneath them
Like a good mat,
As if they picked the place
And then sat.
You walk around one
As if he were the City Hall
After that.

If male,
A cat is apt to sing on a major scale;
This concert is for everybody, this
Is wholesale.
For a baton, he wields a tail.
(He is also found,
When happy, to resound
With an enclosed and private sound.)

A cat condenses.
He pulls in his tail to go under bridges,
And himself to go under fences.
Cats fit
In any size box or kit;
And if a large pumpkin grew under one,
He could arch over it.

When everyone else is just ready to go out,
The cat is just ready to come in.
He's not where he's been.
Cats sleep fat and walk thin.

ROSALIE MOORE

The Rabbit

I see a rabbit drinking at a stream,
I know it wants to run from me, tense
           as it may seem,
But some unknown force makes it stay
           right there and sit,
The same curiosity that makes me keep
           watching it.

PHILIP McINTYRE, JR. Age 12 United States

The Hunters

There were but two beneath the sky —
The thing I came to kill, and I.

I, under covert, quietly
Watched him sense eternity

From quivering brush to pointed nose . . .
My gun to shoulder level rose.

And then I felt (I could not see)
Far off a Hunter watching me.

I slowly put my rifle by,
For there were two who had to die —
The thing I wished to kill, and I.

FLORENCE B. FREEDMAN

Some Brown Sparrows

Some brown sparrows who live
in the Bronx Zoo visit often
the captive Victoria Crested
Pheasant, visit captive Peacocks,
Cockatoos. They fly through bars
to visit also monkeys, jackals,
bears. They delouse themselves in
cage dust, shaking joyously;
they hunt for bread crumbs, seeds
or other tidbits. Briefly,
they lead free sparrow lives
and fly free.

BRUCE FEARING

Two Performing Elephants

He stands with his forefeet on the drum
and the other, the old one, the pallid hoary female
must creep her great bulk beneath the bridge of him.

On her knees, in utmost caution
all agog, and curling up her trunk
she edges through without upsetting him.
Triumph! the ancient, pig-tailed monster!

When her trick is to climb over him
with what shadow-like slow carefulness
she skims him, sensitive
as shadows from the ages gone and perished
in touching him, and planting her round feet.

While the wispy, modern children, half-afraid,
watch silent. The looming of the hoary, far-gone ages
is too much for them.

D. H. LAWRENCE

Madman

He was caged up —
Caged like a mad bull.
He had no friends
Except
The cold touch
Of steel
On the bars.

He was kept
Alive
By the warm touch
Of sunlight
Through the bars.

BILL O'SHEA Age 10 Australia

Death of a Bird

After those first days
When we had placed him in his iron cage
And made a space for him
From such

Outrageous cage of wire,
Long and shallow, where the sunlight fell
Through the air, onto him;
After

He had been fed for three days
Suddenly, in that sunlight before noon
He was dead with no
Pretense.

He did not say goodbye,
He did not say thankyou, but he died then
Lying flat on the rigid
Wires

Of his cage, his gold
Beak shut tight, which once in hunger had
Opened as a trap
And then

Swiftly closed again,
Swallowing quickly what I had given him;
How can I say I am sorry
He died.

Seeing him lie there dead,
Death's friend with death, I was angry he
Had gone without pretext or warning
With no

Suggestion first he should go,
Since I had fed him, then put wires round him,
Bade him hop across
The bars of my hands.

I asked him only that
He should desire his life. He had become
Of us a black friend with
A gold mouth

Shrilly singing through
The heat. The labor of the black bird! I
Cannot understand why
He is dead.

I bury him familiarly.
His heritage is a small brown garden.
Something is added to the everlasting earth;
From my mind a space is taken away.

JON SILKIN

Bats

A bat is born
Naked and blind and pale.
His mother makes a pocket of her tail
And catches him. He clings to her long fur
By his thumbs and toes and teeth.
And then the mother dances through the night
Doubling and looping, soaring, somersaulting —
Her baby hangs on underneath.
All night, in happiness, she hunts and flies.
Her high sharp cries
Like shining needlepoints of sound
Go out into the night and, echoing back,
Tell her what they have touched.
She hears how far it is, how big it is,
Which way it's going:
She lives by hearing.
The mother eats the moths and gnats she catches
In full flight; in full flight
The mother drinks the water of the pond
She skims across. Her baby hangs on tight.
Her baby drinks the milk she makes him
In moonlight or starlight, in mid-air.
Their single shadow, printed on the moon
Or fluttering across the stars,
Whirls on all night; at daybreak
The tired mother flaps home to her rafter.
The others all are there.
They hang themselves up by their toes,
They wrap themselves in their brown wings.
Bunched upside-down, they sleep in air.
Their sharp ears, their sharp teeth, their quick sharp faces
Are dull and slow and mild.
All the bright day, as the mother sleeps,
She folds her wings about her sleeping child.

RANDALL JARRELL

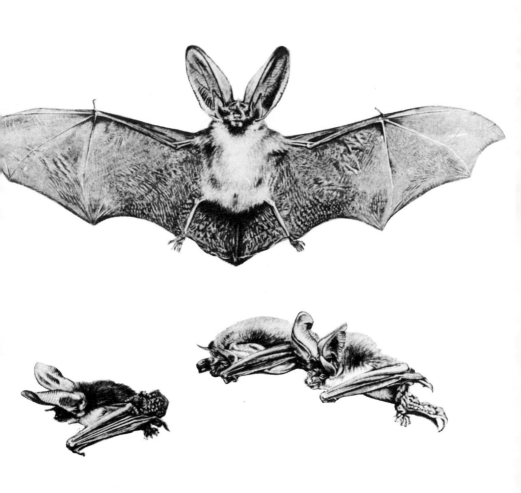

Janet Waking

Beautifully Janet slept
Till it was deeply morning. She woke then
And thought about her dainty-feathered hen,
To see how it had kept.

One kiss she gave her mother,
Only a small one gave she to her daddy
Who would have kissed each curl of his shining baby;
No kiss at all for her brother.

"Old Chucky, old Chucky!" she cried,
Running across the world upon the grass
To Chucky's house, and listening. But alas,
Her Chucky had died.

transforming   It was a transmogrifying bee
Came droning down on Chucky's old bald head
And sat and put the poison. It scarcely bled,
But how exceedingly

And purply did the knot
Swell with the venom and communicate
Its rigor! Now the poor comb stood up straight
But Chucky did not.

So there was Janet
Kneeling on the wet grass, crying her brown hen
(Translated far beyond the daughters of men)
To rise and walk upon it.

And weeping fast as she had breath
Janet implored us, "Wake her from her sleep!"
And would not be instructed in how deep
Was the forgetful kingdom of death.

JOHN CROWE RANSOM

Duck-Chasing

I spied a very small brown duck
Riding the swells of the sea
Like a rocking-chair. "Little duck!"
I cried. It paddled away,
I paddled after it. When it dived,
Down I dived: too smoky was the sea,
We were lost. It surfaced
In the west, I torpedoed west
And when it dived I dived,
And we were lost and lost and lost
In the slant smoke of the sea.
When I came floating up on it
From the side, like a deadman,
And yelled suddenly, it took off,
It skimmed the swells as it ascended,
Brown wings burning and flashing
In the sun as the sea it rose over
Burned and flashed underneath it.
I did not see the little duck again.
Duck-chasing is a game like any game.
When it is over it is all over.

GALWAY KINNELL

The Sloth

In moving-slow he has no Peer.
You ask him something in his ear;
He thinks about it for a Year;

And, then, before he says a Word
There, upside down (unlike a Bird)
He will assume that you have Heard —

A most Ex-as-per-at-ing Lug.
But should you call his manner Smug,
He'll sigh and give his Branch a Hug;

Then off again to Sleep he goes,
Still swaying gently by his Toes,
And you just *know* he knows he knows.

THEODORE ROETHKE

The Serpent

There was a Serpent who had to sing.
There was. There was.
He simply gave up Serpenting.
Because. Because.
He didn't like his Kind of Life;
He couldn't find a proper Wife;
He was a Serpent with a soul;
He got no Pleasure down his Hole.
And so, of course, he had to Sing,
And Sing he did, like Anything!
The Birds, they were, they were Astounded;
And various Measures Propounded
To stop the Serpent's Awful Racket:
They bought a Drum. He wouldn't Whack it.
They sent — you always send — to Cuba
And got a Most Commodious Tuba;
They got a Horn, they got a Flute,
But Nothing would suit.
He said, "Look, Birds, all this is futile:
I do *not* like to Bang or Tootle."
And then he cut loose with a Horrible Note
That practically split the Top of his Throat.
"You see," he said, with a Serpent's Leer,
"I'm Serious about my Singing Career!"
And the Woods Resounded with many a Shriek
As the Bird flew off to the End of Next Week.

THEODORE ROETHKE

The Lady and the Bear

A Lady came to a Bear by a Stream.
"O why are you fishing that way?
Tell me, dear Bear, there by the Stream,
Why are you fishing that way?"

"I am what is known as a Biddly Bear —
That's why I'm fishing this way.
We Biddly's are Pee-culiar Bears.
And so — I'm fishing this way.

"And besides, it seems there's a Law:
A most, most exactious Law
Says a Bear
Doesn't dare
Doesn't dare
Doesn't DARE
Use a Hook or a Line,
Or an old piece of Twine,
Not even the end of his Claw, Claw, Claw,
Not even the end of his Claw.
Yes, a Bear has to fish with his Paw, Paw, Paw.
A Bear has to fish with his Paw."

"O it's Wonderful how with a flick of your Wrist,
You can fish out a fish, out a fish, out a fish,
If I were a fish I just couldn't resist
You, when you are fishing that way, that way,
When you are fishing that way."

And at that the Lady slipped from the Bank
And fell in the Stream still clutching a Plank,
But the Bear just sat there until she Sank;
As he went on fishing his way, his way,
As he went on fishing his way.

THEODORE ROETHKE

The Miser and the Mouse

To a Mouse says a Miser, "My dear Mr. Mouse,
Pray what may you please for to want in my House?"
Says the Mouse, "Mr. Miser, pray keep yourself quiet,
You are safe in your Person, your Purse, and your Diet:
A Lodging I want, which ev'n you may afford,
But none wou'd come here to beg, borrow, or board."

CHRISTOPHER SMART

A Sonnet on a Monkey

O lovely O most charming pug
Thy graceful air and heavenly mug
The beauties of his mind do shine
And every bit is shaped so fine
Your very tail is most divine
Your teeth is whiter than the snow
beau, handsome
man
You are a great buck and a bow
Your eyes are of so fine a shape
More like a christians than an ape.
His cheeks is like the roses blume
Your hair is like the ravens plume
His noses cast is of the roman
He is a very pretty weoman
I could not get a rhyme for roman
And was obliged to call it weoman.

MARJORY FLEMING

The Mad Gardener's Song

He thought he saw an Elephant,
    That practiced on a fife:
He looked again, and found it was
    A letter from his wife.
"At length I realize," he said,
    "The bitterness of Life!"

He thought he saw a Buffalo
    Upon the chimney-piece:
He looked again, and found it was
    His Sister's Husband's Niece,
"Unless you leave this house," he said,
    "I'll send for the Police!"

He thought he saw a Rattlesnake
    That questioned him in Greek:
He looked again, and found it was
    The Middle of Next Week.
"The one thing I regret," he said,
    "Is that it cannot speak!"

He thought he saw a Banker's Clerk
    Descending from the bus:
He looked again, and found it was
    A Hippopotamus.
"If this should stay to dine," he said,
    "There won't be much for us!"

He thought he saw a Kangaroo
    That worked a coffee-mill:
He looked again, and found it was
    A Vegetable-Pill.
"Were I to swallow this," he said,
    "I should be very ill!"

He thought he saw a Coach-and-Four
    That stood beside his bed:
He looked again, and found it was
    A Bear without a Head.

"Poor thing," he said, "poor silly thing!
   It's waiting to be fed!"

He thought he saw an Albatross
   That fluttered round the lamp:
He looked again, and found it was
   A Penny-Postage-Stamp.
"You'd best be getting home," he said,
   "The nights are very damp!"

He thought he saw a Garden-Door
   That opened with a key:
He looked again, and found it was
   A Double Rule of Three:
"And all its mystery," he said,
   "Is clear as day to me!"

He thought he saw an Argument
   That proved he was the Pope:
He looked again, and found it was
   A Bar of Mottled Soap.
"A fact so dread," he faintly said,
   "Extinguishes all hope!"

LEWIS CARROLL

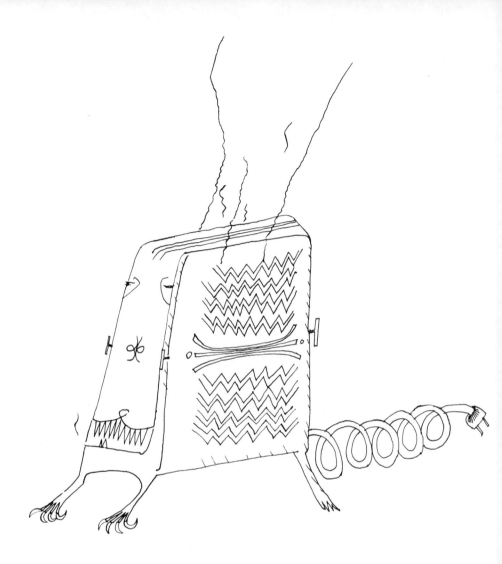

The Toaster

A silver-scaled Dragon with jaws flaming red
Sits at my elbow and toasts my bread.
I hand him fat slices, and then, one by one,
He hands them back when he sees they are done.

WILLIAM JAY SMITH

Steam Shovel

The dinosaurs are not all dead.
I saw one raise its iron head
To watch me walking down the road
Beyond our house today.
Its jaws were dripping with a load
Of earth and grass that it had cropped.
It must have heard me where I stopped,
Snorted white steam my way,
And stretched its long neck out to see,
And chewed, and grinned quite amiably.

CHARLES MALAM

The Garden Hose

In the gray evening
I see a long green serpent
With its tail in the dahlias.

It lies in loops across the grass
And drinks softly at the faucet.

I can hear it swallow.

BEATRICE JANOSCO

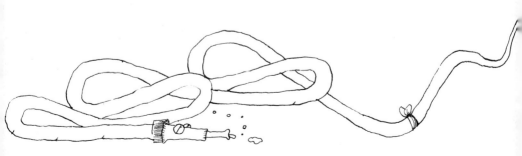

CHRISTIAN MORGENSTERN Translated from the German by Max Knight

he discovers treasure after treasure.
as himself an artist of renown
one room's walls with paintings upside down;
Palmstroem knows this, and he fills with pleasure

for they are transposed to fairyland.
may find unexpected recognition,
upper hand reversed with lower hand,
Pictures hung in upside-down position,

Pictures

Pictures

Pictures hung in upside-down position,
upper hand reversed with lower hand,
may find unexpected recognition,
for they are transposed to fairyland.

Palmstroem knows this, and he fills with pleasure
one room's walls with paintings upside down;
as himself an artist of renown
he discovers treasure after treasure.

CHRISTIAN MORGENSTERN Translated from the German by Max Knight

The Daynight Lamp

Korf invents a daynight lamp
which, as soon as operated,
turns the brightest day
into night.

When he demonstrates it on the ramp
of Convention Hall, no expert may
gainsay, if he's not opinionated,
that one finds it quite ...

(darkness falls upon the sunlit day;
delegates are clapping, fascinated,
and one calls to Butler Bramp:
"Turn the light on!") ... that one finds it quite

evident that the invented lamp
will indeed when operated
turn the brightest day
into night.

CHRISTIAN MORGENSTERN Translated from the German by Max Knight

I Meant To Do My Work Today

I meant to do my work today —
    But a brown bird sang in the apple-tree,
And a butterfly flitted across the field,
    And all the leaves were calling me.

And the wind went sighing over the land,
    Tossing the grasses to and fro,
And a rainbow held out its shining hand —
    So what could I do but laugh and go?

RICHARD LeGALLIENNE

Answer July

Answer July —
Where is the Bee —
Where is the Blush —
Where is the Hay?

Ah, said July —
Where is the Seed —
Where is the Bud —
Where is the May —
Answer Thee — Me —

Nay — said the May —
Show me the Snow —
Show me the Bells —
Show me the Jay!

Quibbled the Jay —
Where be the Maize —
Where be the Haze —
Where be the Bur?
Here — said the Year —

EMILY DICKINSON

A City Garden in April

DAFFODILS

Yellow telephones
in a row in the garden
are ringing,
shrill with light.

Old-fashioned spring
brings earliest models out
each April the same,
naïve and classical.

Look into the yolk-
colored mouthpieces
alert with echoes.
Say hello to time.

MAY SWENSON

I Saw . . .

I saw a green beetle climb crippled grass.
I saw the white speck of a dying butterfly.
I saw grass tops and seedy heads chatter and rustle.
I saw crippled grass bend oldly forward.
I saw yellow flowers in a buttercup wind.
I saw tinker-tailor grass bending in a greasy wind.

S. KERSHAW Age 10 New Zealand

Thief in the Night

Last night a thief came to me
  And struck at me with something dark.
I cried, but no one heard me,
  I lay dumb and stark.

When I awoke this morning
  I could find no trace:
Perhaps 'twas a dream of warning.
  For I've lost my peace.

D. H. LAWRENCE

Winter Morning

This smoky winter morning —
do not despise the green jewel shining among the twigs
because it is a traffic light.

CHARLES REZNIKOFF

The New Moon

Just three days old,
  the moon, and it's all warped and bent,
    How keen the cold!

ISSA Translated from the Japanese by Harold G. Henderson

What Did I Dream?

What did I dream? I do not know —
   The fragments fly like chaff.
Yet, strange, my mind was tickled so
   I cannot help but laugh.

Pull the curtains close again,
   Tuck me grandly in;
Must a world of humor wane
   Because birds begin

Complaining in a fretful tone,
   Rousing me from sleep —
The finest entertainment known,
   And given rag-cheap?

ROBERT GRAVES

Someone Else

In my new clothing
   I feel so different
   I must
Look like someone else

BASHO

The Red Wheelbarrow

so much depends
upon

a red wheel
barrow

glazed with rain
water

beside the white
chickens

WILLIAM CARLOS WILLIAMS

Sowing

It was a perfect day
For sowing; just
As sweet and dry was the ground
As tobacco-dust.

I tasted deep the hour
Between the far
Owl's chuckling first soft cry
And the first star.

A long stretched hour it was;
Nothing undone
Remained; the early seeds
All safely sown.

And now, hark at the rain,
Windless and light,
Half a kiss, half a tear,
Saying good-night.

EDWARD THOMAS

Sowing Beans

One for the mouse, one for the crow,
One to rot, one to grow.

TRADITIONAL

Intery, Mintery

INTERY, mintery, cutery, corn,
Apple seed and briar thorn;
Wire, briar, limber lock,
Five geese in a flock,
Sit and sing by a spring,
O-U-T, and in again.

TRADITIONAL

Ploughing on Sunday

The white cock's tail
Tosses in the wind.
The turkey-cock's tail
Glitters in the sun.

Water in the fields.
The wind pours down.
The feathers flare
And bluster in the wind.

Remus, blow your horn!
I'm ploughing on Sunday,
Ploughing North America.
Blow your horn!

Tum-ti-tum,
Ti-tum-tum-tum!
The turkey-cock's tail
Spreads to the sun.

The white cock's tail
Streams to the moon.
Water in the fields.
The wind pours down.

WALLACE STEVENS

F for Fig

F for fig,
I for jig, and
N for knuckle bones,
I for John the waterman, and
S for sack of stones.

TRADITIONAL

Answers to Puzzles and Riddles

Page 7   **Two Anglo-Saxon Riddles**

1   Ice   2   Crows

What Am I?

1   Glasses   2   In a mirror

Page 8   **Who's Who?**

1   Noah   2   If the man points at the son of
                                      his father's son, he is pointing
                                      at his own son.

3   Dick is John's grandson.

What's Where?

In fir tar is,
In oak none is,
In mud eels are,
In clay none are,
Goats eat ivy;
Mares eat oats.

Page 10   **What's Going on Here?**

The man who collected the poem has this explanation:
Rise up, Dominie Praeceptor, out of your bed; put on your
breeches and your slippers . . . come and see! The cat has jumped
into the fire, run upstairs with a burning coal on her back, and
without absolution . . .
The Devonshire explanation is that a farmer who was a snob
wished to teach his servants Latin. When calamity overtook the
cat, the farmer could not understand what his servants were
shouting.

A Curious Inscription

By adding E, you will arrive at:
              Persevere ye perfect men,
              Ever keep these precepts ten.
—that is, the Ten Commandments.

A Cockney Alphabet

A	'Ay for 'orses	N	'En for eggs
B	Beef or mutton	O	Over my dead body
C	Seaforth Highlanders	P	Pee for a penny
D	Deef or dumb	Q	Queue for the flicks
E	'Eave a brick	R	'Alf a mo'
F	Effervescence	S	As for you . . .
G	Chief of Police	T	Tea for two
H	'Ate ye for it	U	Euphemism
I	'Igh falutin'	V	Vive la France
J	Jaffa oranges	W	Double you for a pound
K	Cafe for a cuppa	X	Eggs for breakfast
L	'Ell for leather	Y	Wife or girl-friend?
M	Emphasis	Z	'S head for 'is 'at.

Page 30   Tall Tales

1. One watches cells and the other sells watches.
2. One pours with rain and the other roars with pain.
3. One is a raving showman and the other is a shaving Roman.
4. Because the adder 'ad 'er 'andkerchief.
5. Only the nose knows.
6. Because it saw the skylark.
7. No, but the tomato can.
8. 'Ark.
9. I haven't a notion. (an ocean)

List of Illustrations

(*Acknowledgements continued*)

E. P. Dutton & Company, Inc.: For "I Wish That My Room Had a Floor" by Gelett Burgess. From *A Century of Humorous Verse*, edited by Roger L. Green. Everyman's Library Edition. Reprinted by permission of E. P. Dutton & Co., Inc.

Norma Millay Ellis: For "Counting Out Rhyme" by Edna St. Vincent Millay. From *Collected Poems*, Harper & Row. Copyright 1928, 1955 by Edna St. Vincent Millay and Norma Millay Ellis.

Faber and Faber Ltd.: For "My Father" by Ted Hughes, from *Meet My Folks!* Reprinted by permission of Faber and Faber Ltd.

Harcourt, Brace & World, Inc.: For "1(a" (copyright 1958 by E. E. Cummings) and "n" (copyright 1952 by E. E. Cummings) from *95 Poems* by E. E. Cummings. For "Buffalo Bill's" (copyright 1923, 1954 by E. E. Cummings) and "r-p-o-p-h-e-s-s-a-g-r" (copyright 1935 by E. E. Cummings; copyright 1963 by Marion Morehouse Cummings) from *Poems 1923-1954* by E. E. Cummings. For "Me up at does" from *73 Poems* by E. E. Cummings. Copyright 1963 by Marion Morehouse Cummings. For "To Look at Anything" from *The Living Seed* by John Moffitt. © 1961 by John Moffitt. For "Buffalo Dusk" from *Smoke and Steel* by Carl Sandburg. Copyright 1920 by Harcourt, Brace & World, Inc.; copyright 1948 by Carl Sandburg. For "Digging for China" from *Things of This World* by Richard Wilbur. © 1956 by Richard Wilbur. All reprinted by permission of Harcourt, Brace & World, Inc.

Harper & Row, Publishers, Inc.: For "The Ballad of Rudolph Reed" from *Selected Poems* by Gwendolyn Brooks. Copyright © 1960 by Gwendolyn Brooks Blakely. Reprinted by permission of Harper & Row, Publishers.

Holt, Rinehart and Winston, Inc.: For "Steam Shovel" from *Upper Pasture* by Charles Malam. Copyright © 1930, 1958 by Charles Malam. Reprinted by permission of Holt, Rinehart and Winston, Inc.

Houghton Mifflin Company: For "Duck Chasing" by Galway Kinnell from *What a Kingdom It Was.* For "Roll a Rock Down" by Henry Herbert Knibbs from *Song of the Trail.* All reprinted by permission of Houghton Mifflin Company.

Beatrice Janosco: For "The Garden Hose" by Beatrice Janosco. Reprinted by permission of the author.

Little, Brown and Company: For "Answer July" from *The Complete Poems of Emily Dickinson*, edited by Thomas H. Johnson. Copyright 1935 by Martha Dickinson Bianchi, © renewed 1963 by Mary L. Hampson. For "What's What" by Alastair Reid, from *Oddments, Inklings, Omens, Moments.* Copyright © 1957 by Alastair Reid, originally appeared in *The New Yorker.* For "Counting" from *Ounce Dice Trice* by Alastair Reid. Copyright © 1958 by Alastair Reid and Ben Shahn. For "The Toaster" by William Jay Smith from *Laughing Time.* Copyright 1955 by William Jay Smith. All reprinted by permission of Atlantic, Little, Brown and Company.

The Macmillan Company: For "The Hunters" by Florence Freedman from *Creatures in Verse.* Copyright © The Macmillan Company 1965. For "Bats" from *The Lost World* by Randall Jarrell. Copyright © by The Macmillan Company 1964. For "Daniel" from *Complete Poems* by Vachel Lindsay. Copyright © 1920 by The Macmillan Company, renewed 1952 by Elizabeth C. Lindsay. For "The High School Band" from *The Self-Made Man* by Reed Whittemore. Copyright © by Reed Whittemore 1956, 1957, 1958, 1959. For "Two Songs of a Fool" from *Collected Poems* by William Butler Yeats. Copyright 1919 by The Macmillan Company and renewed 1946 by Bertha Georgia Yeats. All reprinted by permission of The Macmillan Company.

New Directions Publishing Corporation: For "Winter Morning" from *By the Waters of Manhattan* by Charles Reznikoff. Copyright 1934 by The Objectivist Press. Reprinted by permission of New Directions Publishing Corporation and *San Francisco Review.* For "The Red Wheelbarrow" from *Collected Earlier Poems* by William Carlos Williams. Copyright 1938, 1951 by William Carlos Williams. For "Children's Games" II and III, and "Perpetuum Mobile" from *Pictures from Breughel and Other Poems* by William Carlos Williams. Copyright 1955, © 1962 by William Carlos Williams. All reprinted by permission of New Directions Publishing Corporation.

124

The New Yorker Magazine, Inc.: For "Catalog" by Rosalie Moore. Reprinted by permission; copyright © 1940, 1968. The New Yorker Magazine, Inc.

Oxford University Press: For "Child's Bouncing Song" by Tony Connor from *Poems by Austin Clarke, Tony Connor and Charles Tomlinson,* published by Oxford University Press.

Penguin Books Ltd.: For "Two Anglo-Saxon Riddles" translated from the Anglo-Saxon by Michael Alexander.

Peter Pauper Press, Inc.: For "Someone Else" by Basho and "But If" by Buson from *The Four Seasons.* For "Loneliness" by Basho from *Cherry Blossoms.* Published by Peter Pauper Press, Inc.

Random House, Inc.—Alfred A. Knopf, Inc.: For "Dreams" from *The Dream Keeper* by Langston Hughes. Copyright 1932 and 1960 by Langston Hughes. For "Portrait of the Foot" by John Logan. For "Janet Waking" from *Selected Poems* by John Crowe Ransom. Copyright 1927 and renewed 1955 by John Crowe Ransom. For "Life Is Motion" and "Ploughing on Sunday" from *The Collected Poems of Wallace Stevens.* Copyright 1923 and renewed 1951 by Wallace Stevens. For "The Little Cart" from *Translations from the Chinese* by Arthur Waley. Copyright 1919 and renewed 1947 by Arthur Waley. All reprinted by permission of Alfred A. Knopf, Inc.

Read Magazine: For "Foul Shot" by Edwin A. Hoey. Special reprint permission granted by *Read* Magazine, published by American Education Publications/A Xerox Company, Columbus, Ohio. (Volume II, No. 9, January 1, 1962).

Justin St. John: For "Holes" by Justin St. John.

Charles Scribner's Sons: For "The Centaur" from *Poems To Solve* by May Swenson. For "A City Garden in April: Number 3, Daffodils" from *Half Sun Half Sleep* by May Swenson. Reprinted by permission of Charles Scribner's Sons.

Simon and Schuster, Inc.: For "My Uncle Jack" by David Amey, "The Doors" by Brian Andrews, "I Saw . . ." by S. Kershaw, "The Rabbit" by Philip McIntyre, and "Madman" by Bill O'Shea, all from *Miracles,* collected by Richard Lewis. Copyright © 1966 by Richard Lewis. All reprinted by permission of Simon and Schuster.

Smithsonian Institution: For "Rising of the Buffalo Men" translated by Francis LaFlesche from Part II ("The Rite of Vigil") of a four part monograph "The Osage Tribe," from the 39th *Annual Report of the Bureau of American Ethnology.* Published by the Smithsonian Institution.

Mrs. Myfanwy Thomas: For "Sowing" by Edward Thomas from *Collected Poems.*

University of California Press: For "The Daynight Lamp" and "Pictures" from *The Gallows Songs* by Christian Morgenstern. Translated by Max Knight. Copyright © 1963 by Max E. Knight. Reprinted by permission of the University of California Press.

The Viking Press, Inc.: For "Thief in the Night" and "Two Performing Elephants" by D. H. Lawrence. Both from *The Complete Poems of D. H. Lawrence,* Volume I, edited by Vivian de Sola Pinto and F. Warren Roberts. Copyright 1920 by B. W. Huebsch, Inc., renewed 1948 by Frieda Lawrence. Reprinted by permission of The Viking Press, Inc.

Wesleyan University Press: For "The Base Stealer" by Robert Francis. Copyright © 1948 by Robert Francis. Reprinted from *The Orb Weaver,* by Robert Francis. For "Death of a Bird," Copyright 1958 by Jon Silkin. Reprinted from *Poems New and Selected,* by Jon Silkin. For "Depressed by a Book of Bad Poetry, I Walk Toward an Unused Pasture and Invite the Insects To Join Me," copyright © 1961 by James Wright. Reprinted from *The Branch Will Not Break,* by James Wright. All reprinted by permission of Wesleyan University Press, Inc.

The World Publishing Company: For "Magic Song" and "The Old Man's Song" from *The Book of the Eskimos* by Peter Freuchen. Copyright © 1961 by Peter Freuchen Estate. Both reprinted by permission of The World Publishing Company.

Every effort has been made to trace owners of copyrighted material, but in some cases this has not proved possible. The publishers will be glad to hear from any further owners of copyrighted material reproduced in *Voices* and to arrange payment of appropriate permission fees.

Index of Titles and Poets